CREATE-A-FUT

WRITING A SCIENCE-FICTIO

Written by Eleanor W. Hoomes, Ph.D.

Cover Design and Text Illustration by Karen Sigler

ACKNOWLEDGEMENTS

My students in the Heard Enrichment Program (HEP) in Heard County, Georgia, have been of immeasurable help in preparing and polishing *Create-a-Future.* They have been willing "guinea pigs" as I have tried out all the various activities in the unit on them over the past few years. Thank you, HEP students!

My daughter, Angela Hoomes, has provided valuable help in the preparation of *Create-a-Future.* A science-fiction "nut," she has made suggestions and "tested" the activities on herself.

ISBN 1-56644-018-1

Printed in the U.S.A.

EDUCATIONAL IMPRESSIONS, INC.
Hawthorne, New Jersey 07507

Contents

Introduction to the Teacher

Students like to create, write, and share stories; however, they can be baffled and become resentful when told to write a short story without being shown how to write one. Not knowing where nor how to begin, much less how to develop and end, they often write one skimpy paragraph and call it a short story. Conversely, when they are led through the structure of a story step by step, they often surprise themselves with the results.

Wise teachers capitalize on popular culture in the classroom. They begin with what is already familiar and interesting to students and use that knowledge and interest as springboards to introduce new knowledge. *Create-a-Future: Writing a Science-Fiction Story* builds on the existing knowledge of and interest in science fiction. The recent popularity of science-fiction movies, such as *Star Wars* and its sequels, *E.T.,* the *Star Trek* movies, and other blockbusters are proof of public interest in science fiction. In addition, science-fiction comic books, magazines, and novels are annual best sellers. In fact, ten percent of the fiction published annually in the United States is science fiction.

Science fiction is more commonly referred to as sf, a somewhat broader term than the old sci-fi or even science fiction. The acronym sf can refer to science fantasy, speculative fantasy, and/or scientific fantabulation in addition to science fiction.

Science fiction finally took shape as a genre in the late nineteenth century; however, there were components of science fiction in many earlier writings. Early in the nineteenth century both Mary Shelly and Edgar Allan Poe fused some scientific speculation into their mainly Gothic stories. Other writers, such as Nathaniel Hawthorne, Herman Melville, and Bulwer Lytton, occasionally used scientific speculation. Jules Verne and H.G. Wells are names closely allied with the development of science fiction. H.G. Wells, probably more than any other writer, helped shape science fiction as a genre.

Today the best sf is literature of ideas and philosophy, a literature which makes readers think. Themes which deal with personal integrity, human relationships, other life forms and cultures, and our relationship to and responsibility for the technology we create are found in current sf. Sf serves to help students to examine the possibilities of the future, to stretch their minds and imaginations, to free them from the limitations of the present, and to lead them into the vast possibilities of the future. SF shows readers alternative futures which are interesting within themselves, but it also shows them ways of dealing with a changing future. Changes are inevitable in all lives; often these changes bring with them fear and stress.

Sf can give students a springboard for examining, analyzing, and discussing their futures. It also makes an excellent springboard to the study of a variety of subjects—values, the future, sociology, history, technology, philosophy, and biology—however, *Create-a-Future* uses sf to encourage students to be creative, especially in writing.

Children can write—some better than others, of course, but they all have the raw materials needed for creative writing floating around in their lives. *Create-a-Future* is designed to bring order to those raw materials, help students sort and arrange that which is already familiar, and encourage them to use the results to create stories. In the process of creating their stories, students will examine, discuss, and learn many new concepts. The by-products can be as rewarding as the finished stories. *Create-a-Future* may be used as a creative-writing unit, or it may be used in conjunction with a unit on sf literature. With only a few modifications, it can be used with grades 4 through twelve.

Create-a-Future will help develop students' abilities in observing, concluding, recalling, applying, analyzing, synthesizing, evaluating, divergent thinking, and convergent thinking. At the same time it will contribute to the development of their oral, written, and imaginative skills, with the additional advantage of being fun. Finally, it can give students a final product of which they can be proud!

This unit is designed to save thinking and preparation time for teachers and to encourage planned creativity. Some teachers neither need nor want minute descriptions of teaching approaches and objectives while other teachers, because of time limitations, need more detailed instructions. All are capable of modifying an idea to suit their own purposes and most prefer to innovate rather than copy. Therefore, teachers may use *Create-a-Future* any way they wish, with only their imaginations limiting the various possibilities.

Science fiction is a broad and complex literature. I have made an effort to reduce it to a manageable teaching unit, one that students can use as a guide for their own creative writing. In doing so, I have probably made sf seem too simplistic, streamlining and eliminating many of the more complex issues of sf. The options listed at the bottom of some of the Teacher Directions pages and Activity Nos. 13, 14, and 15 suggest topics for older, more advanced students who wish to delve more deeply into the fascinating mazes of sf. With younger and/or less advanced sf students, Activities 8, 9, 10, and 11 can be used as introductions to sf writing before working through Activities 3, 4, and 5.

Behavioral objectives are not included as they are too precise and lengthy to include in a teaching unit of this type. No bibliography is included; however, two books were invaluable in preparing *Create-a-Future*. They are *Science Fiction Reader's Guide,* by L. David Allen, Centennial Press, Lincoln, Nebraska, and *The Science Fiction Encyclopedia,* edited by Peter Nichols, Dolphin Books, Doubleday and Company, Inc., Garden City, New York. Both of these books will provide extensive additional information for teachers who wish to go beyond *Create-a-Future*.

I sincerely hope that *Create-a-Future* will be as educational and as much fun for other teachers and students as it has been for my students and me. If you and your students enjoy using *Create-a-Future*, you might also like to examine other books in the Create-a-Story series: *Create-a-Sleuth, Create Heroes and Villains, Create-a-Comedy, Create-a-Utopia, Create-an-Autobiography, Create-a-Monster* and *Create-a-Fantasy.*

Good luck!

Create

a

Future

Defining and Identifying Science Fiction

Activity No. 1

Teacher Directions

Objectives: To guide students in defining science fiction

To guide students in identifying science fiction

Thinking Skills: Recall

Observation

Application

Analysis

Synthesis

Evaluation

Directions: While most people seem to be able to identify science fiction, very few are able to define it satisfactorily. Direct students to write down what they consider to be a definition of science fiction. When students have finished, have them share their definitions with the class. Then, as a class, arrive at a working definition of science fiction or sf. You might like to refer to the discussion of definitions of sf in *The Science Fiction Encyclopedia,* pages 159–161, or you might prefer to use Webster's definition of science fiction:

> "Science fiction is fiction dealing principally with the impact of actual or imagined scientific development upon society or individuals; also, futuristic fiction using an aspect of science as an essential component of the plot."

Have students identify their favorite sf book (or series or saga), movie, comic book, magazine, short story (or anthology of short stories), and TV show. Discuss their choices and look for recurring titles and reasons.

Options: History of sf

Educational Impressions, Inc.

Defining and Identifying Science Fiction

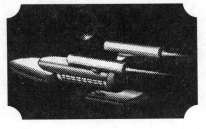

Activity No. 1   **Student Work Sheet**

What is your definition of science fiction?

_____

_____

What is your favorite science-fiction book? Why?

_____

_____

What is your favorite science-fiction movie? Why?

_____

_____

What is your favorite science-fiction comic book? Why?

_____

_____

What is your favorite science-fiction magazine? Why?

_____

_____

What is your favorite science-fiction short story? Why?

_____

_____

What is your favorite science-fiction television show? Why?

_____

_____

Science-Fiction Match

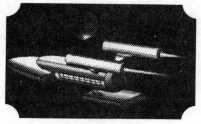

Activity No. 2

Teacher Directions

Objectives:
To introduce students to science fiction

To ascertain the amount of information students already possess about science fiction

To generate interest in studying about and writing science fiction

Thinking Skills:
Recall

Application

Analysis

Evaluation

Directions:
Direct students to match the information listed on the left with the descriptions on the right. After students have finished, give the answers orally and instruct the students to score their own papers. When the exercise is finished, give the students the following interpretation of their scores:

18–20 Correct Answers = Excellent
15–17 Correct Answers = Good
09–14 Correct Answers = Average
0–08 Correct Answers = Below Average

Discuss and/or answer any questions which may arise concerning the matching exercise.

Options:
SF Authors

SF Language

Utopias

Fandom

Answers:
1. R	6. D	11. E	16. N
2. K	7. T	12. I	17. O
3. F	8. S	13. M	18. P
4. B	9. C	14. J	19. Q
5. A	10. H	15. L	20. G

Educational Impressions, Inc.

Science-Fiction Match

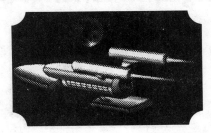

To learn how much you know about fantasy, match the identifying statement in the right column with the correct response in the left column.

___ 1. Princess Leia	A. Science-fiction magazines
___ 2. E.T.	B. Science-fiction awards
___ 3. Spock	C. "Power of good" in *Star Wars*
___ 4. HUGO and NEBULA	D. Screenplay by Stanley Kubrick and Arthur C. Clarke
___ 5. *Galaxy* and *Analog*	E. Author of *The Martian Chronicles*
___ 6. *2001: A Space Odyssey*	F. Has pointed ears
___ 7. Captain Kirk	G. Alikes
___ 8. Black holes	H. A neurotic computer
___ 9 The Force	I. Resulting from sudden hereditary variations
___ 10. HAL 9000	J. Other dimensions
___ 11. Ray Bradbury	K. An alien in need of a telephone
___ 12. Mutants	L. Man-like
___ 13. *Star Trek*	M. TV series of the 1960s
___ 14. Parallel worlds	N. Wrote The Foundation Trilogy
___ 15. Androids	O. Cybernetic organism; a man-machine hybrid
___ 16. Isaac Asimov	P. Author of the Dune series
___ 17. Cyborg	Q. Greatly influenced modern American science fiction
___ 18. Frank Herbert	R. Carrie Fisher
___ 19. Robert Heinlein	S. Results from collapse of star 3 or more times mass of sun
___ 20. Clones	T. Commander of *U.S.S. Enterprise*

Setting and Background

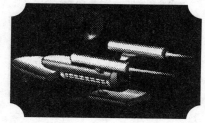

Activity No. 3, A–E

Teacher Directions

Objectives:　To assist students in developing settings and backgrounds for their science-fiction stories

To encourage students to create detailed and believable backgrounds and settings

To help students analyze the choices they make so that they understand the limitations and possibilities of each choice

Thinking Skills:　Observation

Recall

Application

Divergent Thinking

Convergent Thinking

Synthesis

Evaluation

Directions:　In Activity No. 3, A–E, students will develop settings and backgrounds for their stories. You may have students do this individually, in groups, or as a whole class. I have done it all three ways. The way that works best for me is to create the setting and background and to set the parameters as a whole-class activity. This is an excellent time to introduce divergent and convergent thinking in the form of brainstorming and evaluation. When conflicts arise, simply take a vote.

Discuss each question. Because the questions are generally broad, you and your students may wish to make them more specific. Encourage students to understand the repercussions of each choice—both the limitations and the possibilities.

Educational Impressions, Inc.

Time and Place

Activity No. 3, A   **Student Work Sheet**

The setting (time and place) and the background of science fiction are extremely important. Details must be well developed and believable within the framework of the story. The questions in Activity No. 3, A–E, will help you create a setting and a background for your own science-fiction story.

When is your story happening? If you are using multiple times, explain. Why do you choose this time(s)?

_____

_____

_____

_____

_____

_____

Where is your story happening? If the story involves travel, explain all the places that will be used. Explain the climate, topography, ecology, weather, and so on.

_____

_____

_____

_____

_____

_____

_____

_____

_____

_____

_____

Energy and Transportation

Activity No. 3, B

Student Work Sheet

What energy sources are used? How are they used?

_____

_____

_____

_____

_____

_____

_____

What means of transport are used? Describe the transportation network. Start with local transportation and then move step by step to galactic travel. You may wish to draw and label your answers.

_____

_____

_____

_____

_____

_____

_____

_____

_____

_____

_____

_____

Educational Impressions, Inc.

Daily Life

Activity No. 3, C   **Student Work Sheet**

How are children reared? Include information about parents and family, education, housing, food, recreation, society in general, and religion.

_____

_____

_____

_____

_____

_____

_____

_____

How advanced is technology? Include information about medicine and health care along with other technological developments. Do not forget to include labor-saving devices, especially those used on a daily basis.

_____

_____

_____

_____

_____

_____

_____

_____

_____

_____

_____

Goods, Services, and Government

Activity No. 3, D

How are goods and services distributed? What is used for "money"? How is "money" used? What is used in exchange for goods and services? How do people "earn a living"?

_____

_____

_____

_____

_____

_____

_____

_____

How are people governed? Describe the government, starting with the smallest unit and progressing to the largest. Include courts, revenue collection, law enforcement, and other services which might be provided or regulated by a government.

_____

_____

_____

_____

_____

_____

_____

_____

_____

_____

_____

Educational Impressions, Inc.

Leisure and Vocabulary

Activity No. 3, E   **Student Work Sheet**

How much leisure time do people have? How do they spend their leisure time? Discuss sports, the arts, hobbies, and other special interests.

_____

_____

_____

_____

_____

_____

_____

_____

Will you need a special vocabulary in your story? Will you be using made-up words which will need an explanation? If so, list them and their definitions below.

_____

_____

_____

_____

_____

_____

_____

_____

_____

_____

Creating Characters

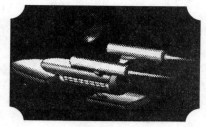

Activity No. 4, A–1   **Teacher Directions**

Objectives: To guide students in determining the characteristics of their science-fiction heroes, heroines, supporting characters, and villains

To encourage students to analyze the ramifications of assigning certain qualities to their characters

To provoke students to question initial reactions based on superficial qualities

Thinking Skills: Recall

Observation

Application

Divergent Thinking

Convergent Thinking

Synthesis

Evaluation

Directions: In Activity No. 4, A–I, students will create characters—main characters, supporting characters, and opponents. You may have them create their characters individually, or you may choose to create the characters together as a class. (See the Teacher Directions of Activity No. 3 for more detailed directions.) Make sure that students understand the limitations and possibilities of assigning certain qualities to their characters.

Options: Stereotypes   Protagonist/Antagonist

Symbols   Conflict

Decision-making   Types of SF (Activity No. 13)

Characterization   Themes in SF (Activity No. 14)

Physical Description

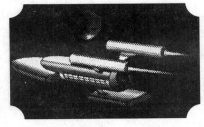

Activity No. 4, A   **Student Work Sheet**

You are now going to create characters to use in your science-fiction story.

The sex, age, race, dress, origin, occupation, values, size and shape, personality, and name all help determine how a character behaves, how other characters respond to him/her, and how a reader responds. Think through what you want your main character (also called hero/heroine or protagonist), supporting characters, and opponents to be or do before you answer the following questions.

What is the name of your main character?

_____

What is the sex of your main character?

_____

How old is your main character?

_____

Is the main characater human or some other form of life or non-life? Why? Explain.

_____

_____

_____

_____

_____

_____

_____

_____

Illustration

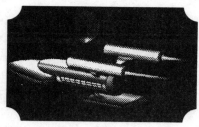

Activity No. 4, B

Student Work Sheet

What is the physical description of the main character of your science-fiction story? Include size, coloring, hair, eyes, and so on. How does the main character dress? Draw and label your main character in the space below.

Educational Impressions, Inc.

Origin and Personality

Activity No. 4, C

Student Work Sheet

How did your main character originate? Where and under what circumstances was your main character born, invented, combined, or created? Explain in detail.

_____

_____

_____

_____

What kind of personality does your main character have?

_____

_____

_____

_____

_____

_____

What special likes and dislikes does your main character have? How do his/her likes and dislikes affect his/her behavior?

_____

_____

_____

_____

_____

_____

_____

Phobias, Occupation, and Values

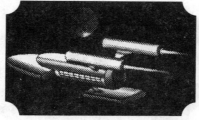

Activity No. 4, D

Student Work Sheet

What phobias, if any, plague your main character? How?

_____

_____

_____

_____

What is the occupation of your main character? Why do you choose this occupation?

_____

_____

_____

_____

_____

_____

What does your main character value? How will your main character's values affect his/her actions?

_____

_____

_____

_____

_____

_____

_____

_____

Educational Impressions, Inc.

Strengths and Weaknesses

Activity No. 4, E

Student Work Sheet

What special strengths might your main character possess? How can these special abilities contribute to the successes of your main character?

_____

_____

_____

_____

_____

_____

_____

What weaknesses might your main character possess? How might these weaknesses contribute to the problems faced by your main character?

_____

_____

_____

_____

_____

_____

_____

_____

_____

Family and Friends

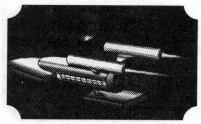

Activity No. 4, F

Student Work Sheet

What kind of family does your main character have? How is family important to your main character? How might family members help or hinder your main character? List family members and explain their roles in your main character's life.

_____

_____

_____

_____

_____

_____

_____

_____

What kind of friends does your main character have? How are they important? List his/her friends and explain their role in your main character's life.

_____

_____

_____

_____

_____

_____

_____

_____

_____

Educational Impressions, Inc.

Motivation and Adventures

Activity No. 4, G

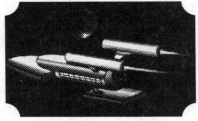

Student Work Sheet

What motivates your main character? How does he/she deal with his/her motivations?

_____

_____

_____

_____

_____

_____

_____

What adventures might your main character have? What kinds of things might he/she do that would make a story interesting?

_____

_____

_____

_____

_____

_____

_____

_____

_____

_____

Supporting Characters

Activity No. 4, H

Student Work Sheet

Who will be the supporting characters in your science-fiction story? Use the questions in
Activity No. 4, A–G, as a guide in creating at least three supporting characters.

_____

_____

_____

_____

_____

_____

_____

_____

_____

_____

_____

_____

_____

_____

_____

_____

_____

_____

_____

_____

_____

Educational Impressions, Inc.

Conflict

Activity No. 4, I

Student Work Sheet

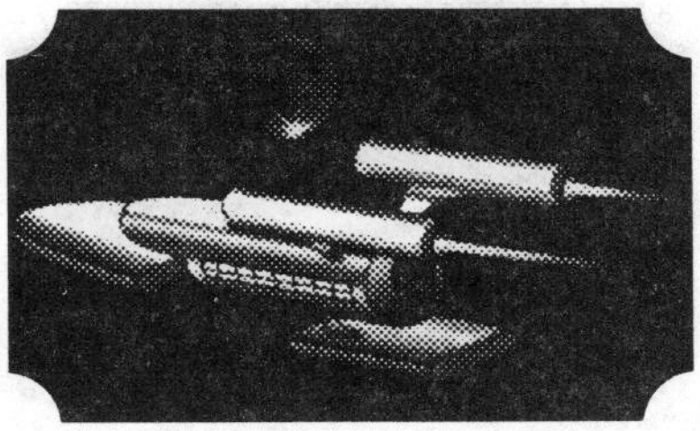

Who (called opponents, villains, or antagonists) or what will oppose your main character or cause trouble in your science-fiction story? The causes of conflict and trouble need not be living organisms; they might be machines or natural forces. Create three causes of trouble for your main character. You might like to use Activity No. 4, A–G, as a guide if you are using humans as sources of conflict.

Writing a Science-Fiction Story

Activity No. 5   **Teacher Directions**

Objectives: To assist students in analyzing the parts of a short story

To teach students the construction of a short story

To engage students in writing science fiction

Thinking Skills: Application

Analysis

Convergent Thinking

Divergent Thinking

Synthesis

Evaluation

Directions: Discuss the following: Why must a story have a beginning, a middle, and an end? What kinds of conflicts might your protagonist encounter? How will the conflicts be resolved? Why would a reader be more intrigued by the use of brains to solve a conflict as opposed to the use of brawn?

Instruct students to write their stories. They will probably prefer to use third person and past tense. Cover the use of direct quotations and any other necessary writing mechanics. After students have finished writing their stories, have them exchange with each other for proofreading. After corrections have been made, have students share their stories aloud.

Options: Conflict

Point of view

Theme

Tone

Good vs. Evil as a literary theme

Writing a Science-Fiction Story

Activity No. 5

Student Work Sheet

You are now ready to write a science-fiction story. Base it upon all the information which you have compiled on creating setting and background in Activity No. 3 and creating characters in Activity No. 4. Treat this science-fiction story as the first in a series of exciting adventures. Remember to use direct conversation and to depict action as it occurs. A short story has three major parts:

1. The beginning, where the characters, setting and background, and situation(s) are introduced;

2. The middle, where complications and conflicts arise (a series of complications and conflicts may be encountered here); and

3. The ending, where the conflicts and complications are resolved.

If you intend to use your characters again, you must leave them alive at the end, in situations which resolve the conflicts and uncomplicate the complications. Then they are capable of appearing in later stories. If possible, use brains instead of brawn to settle problems.

When you finish writing your story, exchange with a classmate. Proofread each other's stories and then correct all errors.

FOLLOW-UP IDEAS:

Make copies of your stories and bind them together into a magazine.

Present your stories to another class in a choral reading or in a reader's theater.

Present your stories to a parents group or to other adult groups in your community.

Other Ways to Use Science Fiction

Activity No. 6–12

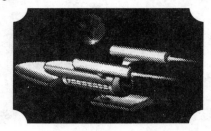

Teacher Directions

Objectives: To provide opportunities for those students who wish to continue writing science fiction

To provide choices for students

Thinking Skills: Observation

Recall

Application

Analysis

Divergent Thinking

Convergent Thinking

Synthesis

Evaluation

Directions: Activities 6 through 11 can be used to extend the Create-a-Future teaching unit, as follow-ups at later dates during the year, before starting Activity No.1, or as individual, one-time writing assignments. No individual directions are given; instead, the student pages are fairly complete within themselves.

Activity No. 6: Other Ways to Use Science Fiction

Activity No. 7: Group-Created Stories

Activity No. 8: How I Spent My Summer Vacation

Activity No. 9: Visitors from Earth

Activity No. 10: Guess What Landed in My Peach Orchard

Activity No. 11: A Rocket to _____

Activity No. 12: I Was Kidnapped by Aliens

Other Ways to Use Science Fiction

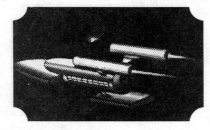

Activity No. 6   **Student Work Sheet**

In addition to writing a short story, you may wish to try some of the following suggestions:

Write a radio script. With appropriate sound effects, the script may be produced for an audience by simply using a screen to conceal the participants from their audience. The script could also be recorded on a tape recorder and then played for the audience. Do not overlook the use of music to achieve dramatic effects.

Write a play. A play is not complete unless it is staged. Producing a play involves more work than producing a radio show because the audience sees the actors. Lines and actions must be learned; whereas, in a radio show the lines can be read. If you have access to a video camera, filming the play can be an interesting experience.

Draw a comic strip. Study comic books so you are thoroughly familiar with all the conventions of comic-book writing.

Write a narrative poem. Treat your material in either a serious or a humorous manner.

Write a song. Set it to music and record it on a tape recorder.

Draw a filmstrip of the story you wrote in Activity No. 6 or write a new story to make into a filmstrip. Record the story on a tape recorder and synchronize the two to show to an audience.

Draw cartoons of your main character. Show him/her in situations which reveal his/her true personality and character.

Write a newspaper article about the exploits of your main character. Use an eye-catching headline. Remember to answer the following questions: Who? What? Why? When? How?

Turn your newspaper account into a TV news bulletin or a TV feature story.

Group-Created Stories

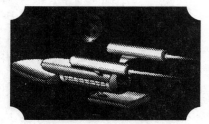

Activity No. 7   **Student Work Sheet**

Using the basic procedures learned in the preceding activities, create group stories using the following process:

Divide into groups of four students. Each member of the group will select one of the following tasks. (You may have to double-up, depending on the number of students in your class.)

1. Create a main character.

2. Create an opponent.

3. Create a setting and background and a basic situation.

4. Create a crisis, conflict(s), and complications.

After you have completed the above assignment individually, return to your group. Put your imaginations to work, using the materials you have created, to create one of the products listed below. Refer to Activity No. 7 for more details.

1. A short story

2. A radio script

3. A play

4. A poem

5. A song

6. A comic strip

7. A filmstrip

8. A cartoon

9. A newspaper, radio, or TV news story

Using your created main character and the main character created by a classmate, co-author a story wherein both star. How do they meet? How do they cooperate or conflict? What adventures do they have together?

How I Spent My Summer Vacation

Activity No. 8   **Student Work Sheet**

The year is 2005. School has just started. Your English teacher has assigned the following topic for the first weekly essay: How I Spent My Summer Vacation. You spent your vacation as the first teenage astronaut for NASA. Answer the following questions and then write an essay or a short story detailing your experiences.

How and why were you chosen? Who, if anyone, went with you?

_____

_____

_____

_____

Where did you go and what did you do?

_____

_____

_____

_____

How did your family and friends react to your being chosen? How have they reacted to you since your return?

_____

_____

_____

What has happened to you since you returned?

_____

_____

_____

Visitors from Earth

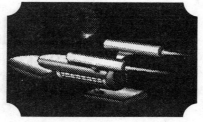

Activity No. 9

Student Work Sheet

The year is 2084. You live in one of the following types of communities:

An underwater city

A satellite city floating above Earth

A colony on Mars

Your grandparents from _____ (city), _____ (state), the United States, Earth, are coming to visit you for the first time. How will you entertain them during their two-week visit with you? Write a story about their visit.

_____

_____

_____

_____

_____

_____

_____

_____

_____

_____

_____

_____

_____

_____

_____

_____

You might wish to write a story about your return visit to your grandparents' home on Earth.

Educational Impressions, Inc.

Guess What Landed in My Peach Orchard

Activity No. 10

Student Work Sheet

You and your friend have just had an exciting adventure. The two of you were camping in your family's peach orchard. At midnight you were awakened by "weird" noises and bright lights. You both ran to investigate. What did you find? What did you and your friend do? What did "they" do? Write a story about your adventure.

_____

_____

_____

_____

_____

_____

_____

_____

_____

_____

_____

_____

_____

_____

_____

_____

_____

_____

A Rocket to _____

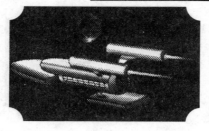

Activity No. 11   **Student Work Sheet**

Your science teacher assigned group projects. You and your two best friends decided to build a rocket—not just a model, but a real working rocket! Answer the following questions and then write a story based on your answers.

How did you build the rocket?

_____

_____

_____

What did it look like when you finished it? Draw and label it on the reverse of this page.

_____

_____

Under what circumstances did it "lift off"?

_____

_____

Where did you go? What did you see? What did you do?

_____

_____

_____

_____

What happened after you returned? What grade did your teacher give you? Why?

_____

_____

_____

I Was Kidnapped by Aliens

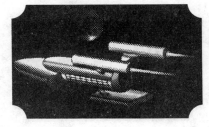

Activity No. 12

Student Work Sheet

You were kidnapped by a couple of aliens. You spent forty-eight hours in captivity before managing to escape. You are now something of a local hero/heroine, with various members of the news media clamoring to interview you. Your parents have consented for you to be interviewed by one person, _____, for his/her
TV show, _____.
He/she asks the following questions. How do you answer them?

What did the aliens look like? What were their names?

_____

_____

Draw and label the aliens for the audience.

I Was Kidnapped by Aliens

Activity No. 12, cont.

Student Work Sheet

Now, start at the beginning. Where were you and what were you doing when you first encountered the aliens? When was this? What was your first reaction? Your second?

_____

_____

_____

_____

_____

_____

How did the aliens take you? How did you communicate with them? How did they communicate with each other?

_____

_____

_____

_____

_____

_____

Where did the aliens take you? How did they get you there? What was the place like?

_____

_____

_____

_____

_____

_____

I Was Kidnapped by Aliens

Activity No. 12, cont.   **Student Work Sheet**

What did the aliens do to you or with you while they held you captive?

_____

_____

_____

_____

_____

Did they offer you food? If so, what? How was it prepared? Did you eat it? What did it taste like?

_____

_____

_____

How did you escape?

_____

_____

_____

_____

What are your feelings now about your adventure?

_____

_____

_____

Follow-Up Activities

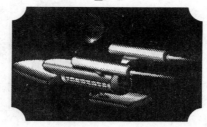

Activity No. 13–15   **Teacher Directions**

Objectives: To provide additional opportunities for advanced science-fiction students

                  To provide additional choices for students

Thinking Skills: Observation

                  Recall

                  Comprehension

                  Application

                  Analysis

                  Divergent Thinking

                  Convergent Thinking

                  Synthesis

                  Evaluation

Directions: Activities 13 through 15 are for older and/or more advanced science-fictions students. They can be used to extend the Create-a-Future teaching unit as follow-ups at later dates during the year, or they may be used as individual, one-time writing assignments. No individual directions are given; instead, the student pages are fairly complete within themselves.

Activity No. 13:   Types of Science Fiction

Activity No. 14:   Themes in Science Fiction

Activity No. 15:   Suggestions for Further Study

Types of Science Fiction

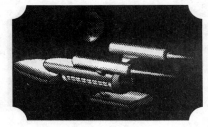

Your imagination—your ability to fantasize about alternate possibilities, your creative potential—is one of the greatest resources you have as a human being. Never fail to use your imagination because you fear that you will lose touch with reality or that others will misunderstand you or laugh at you. You can learn to enjoy and to control the powers of your imagination, and from that enjoyment and control you can learn to create science-fiction stories. The following three activities are suggestions to help you harness that powerful imagination of yours.

According to sf writers and other sf experts, there are several categories of science fiction which overlap and shade into each other. Sometimes there are no clear-cut, distinct lines. Listed below are some of those categories. If you are unfamiliar with any of the terms, check in your library for additional information. Choose a category, research that category, and write a science-fiction story of that type. Use Activities 3, 4, and 5 as a guide.

Space Opera

Hard SF

Hardcore SF

Heroic Fantasy

Pulp SF

Science Fantasy

Soft SF

Sword and Sorcery

Utopias

Themes in Science Fiction

Activity No. 14

The theme of a work of fiction is the main idea, the basis around which a story revolves. A story might have more than one theme. Very often science fiction will deal with universal themes, themes which have appeal to all cultures. Below is a partial list of recurring themes in science fiction. Pick one or more themes and write a science-fiction story based on the theme(s) you have chosen. Use Activities 3, 4, and 5 as a guide.

Overpopulation

Overurbanization

New Man/Mutation

Messiah or Savior

Space Travel and Exploration

Scientific and Technological Gimmickry

Time Travel (Forward or Backward)

Exploration of Human Potential

Ultimate Meaning

Adam and Eve

Alternate Worlds

Lost Worlds

Parallel Worlds

Crime and Punishment

Discovery

Invention

End of the World

Evolution

Fourth Dimension

Genetic Engineering

Colonization of Space

Devolution

Educational Impressions, Inc.

Suggestions for Further Study

Activity No. 15

Student Work Sheet

Females in SF:

Possibly because most early sf was written for males and because most early sf writers were men, females did not fare too well in sf. Most of the roles assigned to females were stereotypes, much more so than in mainstream fiction. Influenced by the feminist movement, the roles of females in sf started to change gradually after the 1960s. Research and analyze the roles of females in early sf and later sf. Are there any differences? Are there any similarities?

Women SF Writers:

In the early days of sf, many women writers used pseudonyms or initials because publishers feared that a largely male audience would not read sf written by women. While today there are approximately nine male sf writers for every female sf writer, women are doing excellent work in the field. The female audience for sf continues to grow. Following is a very brief list of women sf writers. Choose one of them or another female sf writer to explore in depth.

    Ursula K. Le Guin
    J. Hunter Holly (now Joan)
    Andrew North (now André)
    Hilary Bailey
    Jane Gaskell
    Shirley Jackson
    Katherine Kurtz
    Doris Lessing

SF Magazines:

There are many science-fiction magazines; *Extrapolation, Foundations, Science-Fiction Studies, Galaxy, Forum, Isaac Asimov's Science Fiction,* and *Analog* are some examples. Make a compartive study of science-fiction magazines.

SF Movies:

George Melies made the first science-fiction movie, *A Trip to the Moon,* around 1900. Many sf movies have been made since then. Make a study of science-fiction movies. You might like to study sf on television also.

Suggestions for Further Study

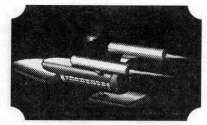

Activity No. 15, cont.

Student Work Sheet

SF as Predictor:

Early science-fiction writers predicted later technological developments, such as television, space travel, atomic submarines, and labor-saving devices. Later writers had some influence on the actual development of space flight. Make a study of the science fiction of such writers as Jules Verne, H.G. Wells, Aldous Huxley, Arthur C. Clarke, Willy Lee, Issac Asimov, Frank Herbert, and Robert Heinlein. Compare their "predictions" with what has already happened and is happening today.

Juvenile SF:

Among the best known, although not the best written, juvenile science fiction was published by the Stratemeyer Syndicate. The first series, featuring the hero Tom Swift, was published between 1910 and 1938 under the name Victor Appleton. The second series, featuring Tom Swift, Jr., was published between 1954 and 1971, with the author given as Victor Appleton, Jr. Actually, several authors wrote the books, but H.G. Garis is generally credited with at least thirty-five titles in the first series. Research the history of juvenile science fiction. Then write a report comparing juvenile and adult science fiction.

Future-Problem-Solving Scenarios:

A part of the Future-Problem-Solving Program is a scenario competition. Many states have state competitions, and there is also a national competition. Winning scenarios, which are basically science-fiction stories, are published in Award-Winning Scenarios.

For information on Future Problem Solving and/or scenario writing, write to:

Dr. Anne B. Crabbe
Future Problem Solving
Coe College
Cedar Rapids, Iowa 52402

Suggestions for Further Study

Activity No. 15, cont.   **Student Work Sheet**

Holocaust Theme:

An often-used theme in science fiction is the world cleared by a holocaust. Only a few people remain to start the living process again. Make a study of the holocaust theme in science fiction. (Although it is not sf, *The Last Flower*, by James Thurber, should also be read.) Follow up by writing your own story.

Robinson Crusoe Theme:

The Robinson Crusoe theme has been used in sf many times. Read Daniel Defoe's *Robinson Crusoe* and then write a science-fiction story using a similar theme. Make yourself the main character.

Nowhere to Go:

The year is 3016. It is now known for certain that no life forms exist anywhere other than Earth. Many experiments to spread life into space from Earth have failed, not because the technology does not exist, but because people cannot or will not adapt psychologically. Write a story showing how Earthlings cope with the situation.

Cryonics, or I Was a Frozen Teenager:

When you were sixteen in 1999, you developed an incurable disease. As your condition worsened, you and your parents decided that cryonics presented a viable alternative to death. So you were frozen. Two hundred years later a cure is discovered for your disease. You are still seventeen when you are unfrozen. Write a story about what your life has been like since you were unfrozen.

TEAR-OUT REPRODUCIBLE STUDENT WORK SHEETS

Defining and Identifying Science Fiction

Activity No. 1

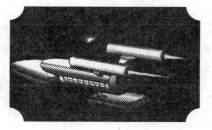

Student Work Sheet

What is your definition of science fiction?

_____

_____

What is your favorite science-fiction book? Why?

_____

_____

What is your favorite science-fiction movie? Why?

_____

_____

What is your favorite science-fiction comic book? Why?

_____

_____

What is your favorite science-fiction magazine? Why?

_____

_____

What is your favorite science-fiction short story? Why?

_____

_____

What is your favorite science-fiction television show? Why?

_____

_____

                    Educational Impressions, Inc.

Science-Fiction Match

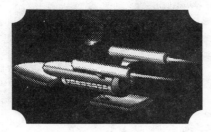

Activity No. 2   **Student Work Sheet**

To learn how much you know about fantasy, match the identifying statement in the right column with the correct response in the left column.

___ 1. Princess Leia	A. Science-fiction magazines
___ 2. E.T.	B. Science-fiction awards
___ 3. Spock	C. "Power of good" in *Star Wars*
___ 4. HUGO and NEBULA	D. Screenplay by Stanley Kubrick and Arthur C. Clarke
___ 5. *Galaxy* and *Analog*	E. Author of *The Martian Chronicles*
___ 6. *2001: A Space Odyssey*	F. Has pointed ears
___ 7. Captain Kirk	G. Alikes
___ 8. Black holes	H. A neurotic computer
___ 9 The Force	I. Resulting from sudden hereditary variations
___ 10. HAL 9000	J. Other dimensions
___ 11. Ray Bradbury	K. An alien in need of a telephone
___ 12. Mutants	L. Man-like
___ 13. *Star Trek*	M. TV series of the 1960s
___ 14. Parallel worlds	N. Wrote The Foundation Trilogy
___ 15. Androids	O. Cybernetic organism; a man-machine hybrid
___ 16. Isaac Asimov	P. Author of the Dune series
___ 17. Cyborg	Q. Greatly influenced modern American science fiction
___ 18. Frank Herbert	R. Carrie Fisher
___ 19. Robert Heinlein	S. Results from collapse of star 3 or more times mass of sun
___ 20. Clones	T. Commander of *U.S.S. Enterprise*

Time and Place

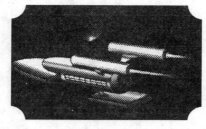

Activity No. 3, A

Student Work Sheet

The setting (time and place) and the background of science fiction are extremely important. Details must be well developed and believable within the framework of the story. The questions in Activity No. 3, A–E, will help you create a setting and a background for your own science-fiction story.

When is your story happening? If you are using multiple times, explain. Why do you choose this time(s)?

_____

_____

_____

_____

_____

_____

Where is your story happening? If the story involves travel, explain all the places that will be used. Explain the climate, topography, ecology, weather, and so on.

_____

_____

_____

_____

_____

_____

_____

_____

_____

_____

_____

Educational Impressions, Inc.

Energy and Transportation

Activity No. 3, B   **Student Work Sheet**

What energy sources are used? How are they used?

_____

_____

_____

_____

_____

_____

What means of transport are used? Describe the transportation network. Start with local transportation and then move step by step to galactic travel. You may wish to draw and label your answers.

_____

_____

_____

_____

_____

_____

_____

_____

_____

_____

_____

_____

Daily Life

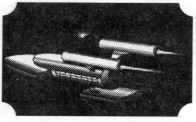

Activity No. 3, C

How are children reared? Include information about parents and family, education, housing, food, recreation, society in general, and religion.

_____

_____

_____

_____

_____

_____

_____

How advanced is technology? Include information about medicine and health care along with other technological developments. Do not forget to include labor-saving devices, especially those used on a daily basis.

_____

_____

_____

_____

_____

_____

_____

_____

_____

_____

Goods, Services, and Government

Activity No. 3, D   **Student Work Sheet**

How are goods and services distributed? What is used for "money"? How is "money" used?
What is used in exchange for goods and services? How do people "earn a living"?

_____

_____

_____

_____

_____

_____

_____

How are people governed? Describe the government, starting with the smallest unit and progressing to the largest. Include courts, revenue collection, law enforcement, and other services
which might be provided or regulated by a government.

_____

_____

_____

_____

_____

_____

_____

_____

_____

_____

Leisure and Vocabulary

Activity No. 3, E

Student Work Sheet

How much leisure time do people have? How do they spend their leisure time? Discuss sports, the arts, hobbies, and other special interests.

_____

_____

_____

_____

_____

_____

_____

_____

Will you need a special vocabulary in your story? Will you be using made-up words which will need an explanation? If so, list them and their definitions below.

_____

_____

_____

_____

_____

_____

_____

_____

_____

_____

_____

Educational Impressions, Inc.

Physical Description

Activity No. 4, A   **Student Work Sheet**

You are now going to create characters to use in your science-fiction story.

The sex, age, race, dress, origin, occupation, values, size and shape, personality, and name all help determine how a character behaves, how other characters respond to him/her, and how a reader responds. Think through what you want your main character (also called hero/heroine or protagonist), supporting characters, and opponents to be or do before you answer the following questions.

What is the name of your main character?

_____

What is the sex of your main character?

_____

How old is your main character?

_____

Is the main characater human or some other form of life or non-life? Why? Explain.

_____

_____

_____

_____

_____

_____

_____

Illustration

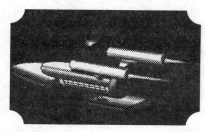

Activity No. 4, B   **Student Work Sheet**

What is the physical description of the main character of your science-fiction story? Include size, coloring, hair, eyes, and so on. How does the main character dress? Draw and label your main character in the space below.

                                   Educational Impressions, Inc.

Origin and Personality

Activity No. 4, C   **Student Work Sheet**

How did your main character originate? Where and under what circumstances was your main character born, invented, combined, or created? Explain in detail.

_____

_____

_____

_____

What kind of personality does your main character have?

_____

_____

_____

_____

_____

What special likes and dislikes does your main character have? How do his/her likes and dislikes affect his/her behavior?

_____

_____

_____

_____

_____

_____

_____

_____

Phobias, Occupation, and Values

Activity No. 4, D

Student Work Sheet

What phobias, if any, plague your main character? How?

_____

_____

_____

_____

What is the occupation of your main character? Why do you choose this occupation?

_____

_____

_____

_____

_____

_____

What does your main character value? How will your main character's values affect his/her actions?

_____

_____

_____

_____

_____

_____

_____

_____

Educational Impressions, Inc.

Strengths and Weaknesses

Activity No. 4, E   **Student Work Sheet**

What special strengths might your main character possess? How can these special abilities contribute to the successes of your main character?

_____

_____

_____

_____

_____

_____

_____

What weaknesses might your main character possess? How might these weaknesses contribute to the problems faced by your main character?

_____

_____

_____

_____

_____

_____

_____

_____

_____

_____

Family and Friends

Activity No. 4, F   **Student Work Sheet**

What kind of family does your main character have? How is family important to your main character? How might family members help or hinder your main character? List family members and explain their roles in your main character's life.

_____

_____

_____

_____

_____

_____

_____

_____

What kind of friends does your main character have? How are they important? List his/her friends and explain their role in your main character's life.

_____

_____

_____

_____

_____

_____

_____

_____

_____

Educational Impressions, Inc.

Motivation and Adventures

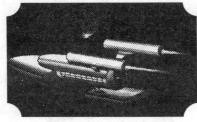

Activity No. 4, G   **Student Work Sheet**

What motivates your main character? How does he/she deal with his/her motivations?

_____

_____

_____

_____

_____

_____

_____

_____

What adventures might your main character have? What kinds of things might he/she do that
would make a story interesting?

_____

_____

_____

_____

_____

_____

_____

_____

_____

Supporting Characters

Activity No. 4, H   **Student Work Sheet**

Who will be the supporting characters in your science-fiction story? Use the questions in
Activity No. 4, A–G, as a guide in creating at least three supporting characters.

_____

_____

_____

_____

_____

_____

_____

_____

_____

_____

_____

_____

_____

_____

_____

_____

_____

_____

_____

Conflict

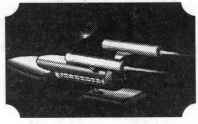

Activity No. 4, I

Student Work Sheet

Who (called opponents, villains, or antagonists) or what will oppose your main character or cause trouble in your science-fiction story? The causes of conflict and trouble need not be living organisms; they might be machines or natural forces. Create three causes of trouble for your main character. You might like to use Activity No. 4, A–G, as a guide if you are using humans as sources of conflict.

_____

_____

_____

_____

_____

_____

_____

_____

_____

_____

_____

_____

_____

_____

_____

_____

_____

_____

_____

Writing a Science-Fiction Story

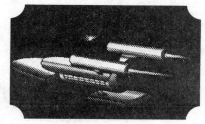

Activity No. 5   **Student Work Sheet**

You are now ready to write a science-fiction story. Base it upon all the information which you have compiled on creating setting and background in Activity No. 3 and creating characters in Activity No. 4. Treat this science-fiction story as the first in a series of exciting adventures. Remember to use direct conversation and to depict action as it occurs. A short story has three major parts:

1. The beginning, where the characters, setting and background, and situation(s) are intro-duced;

2. The middle, where complications and conflicts arise (a series of complications and con-flicts may be encountered here); and

3. The ending, where the conflicts and complications are resolved.

If you intend to use your characters again, you must leave them alive at the end, in situations which resolve the conflicts and uncomplicate the complications. Then they are capable of appearing in later stories. If possible, use brains instead of brawn to settle problems.

When you finish writing your story, exchange with a classmate. Proofread each other's stories and then correct all errors.

FOLLOW-UP IDEAS:

Make copies of your stories and bind them together into a magazine.

Present your stories to another class in a choral reading or in a reader's theater.

Present your stories to a parents group or to other adult groups in your community.

Other Ways to Use Science Fiction

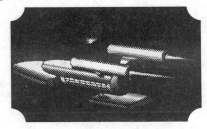

Activity No. 6   **Student Work Sheet**

In addition to writing a short story, you may wish to try some of the following suggestions:

Write a radio script. With appropriate sound effects, the script may be produced for an audience by simply using a screen to conceal the participants from their audience. The script could also be recorded on a tape recorder and then played for the audience. Do not overlook the use of music to achieve dramatic effects.

Write a play. A play is not complete unless it is staged. Producing a play involves more work than producing a radio show because the audience sees the actors. Lines and actions must be learned; whereas, in a radio show the lines can be read. If you have access to a video camera, filming the play can be an interesting experience.

Draw a comic strip. Study comic books so you are thoroughly familiar with all the conventions of comic-book writing.

Write a narrative poem. Treat your material in either a serious or a humorous manner.

Write a song. Set it to music and record it on a tape recorder.

Draw a filmstrip of the story you wrote in Activity No. 6 or write a new story to make into a filmstrip. Record the story on a tape recorder and synchronize the two to show to an audience.

Draw cartoons of your main character. Show him/her in situations which reveal his/her true personality and character.

Write a newspaper article about the exploits of your main character. Use an eye-catching headline. Remember to answer the following questions: Who? What? Why? When? How?

Turn your newspaper account into a TV news bulletin or a TV feature story.

Group-Created Stories

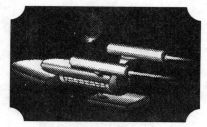

Activity No. 7   **Student Work Sheet**

Using the basic procedures learned in the preceding activities, create group stories using the following process:

Divide into groups of four students. Each member of the group will select one of the following tasks. (You may have to double-up, depending on the number of students in your class.)

   1. Create a main character.

   2. Create an opponent.

   3. Create a setting and background and a basic situation.

   4. Create a crisis, conflict(s), and complications.

After you have completed the above assignment individually, return to your group. Put your imaginations to work, using the materials you have created, to create one of the products listed below. Refer to Activity No. 7 for more details.

   1. A short story

   2. A radio script

   3. A play

   4. A poem

   5. A song

   6. A comic strip

   7. A filmstrip

   8. A cartoon

   9. A newspaper, radio, or TV news story

Using your created main character and the main character created by a classmate, co-author a story wherein both star. How do they meet? How do they cooperate or conflict? What adventures do they have together?

How I Spent My Summer Vacation

Activity No. 8

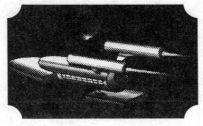

Student Work Sheet

The year is 2005. School has just started. Your English teacher has assigned the following topic for the first weekly essay: How I Spent My Summer Vacation. You spent your vacation as the first teenage astronaut for NASA. Answer the following questions and then write an essay or a short story detailing your experiences.

How and why were you chosen? Who, if anyone, went with you?

_____

_____

_____

_____

Where did you go and what did you do?

_____

_____

_____

_____

_____

How did your family and friends react to your being chosen? How have they reacted to you since your return?

_____

_____

_____

_____

What has happened to you since you returned?

_____

_____

_____

Visitors from Earth

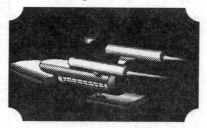

Activity No. 9   **Student Work Sheet**

The year is 2084. You live in one of the following types of communities:

    An underwater city

    A satellite city floating above Earth

    A colony on Mars

Your grandparents from _____ (city), _____ (state), the United States, Earth, are coming to visit you for the first time. How will you entertain them during their two-week visit with you? Write a story about their visit.

_____

_____

_____

_____

_____

_____

_____

_____

_____

_____

_____

_____

_____

_____

_____

_____

You might wish to write a story about your return visit to your grandparents' home on Earth.

Guess What Landed in My Peach Orchard

Activity No. 10   **Student Work Sheet**

You and your friend have just had an exciting adventure. The two of you were camping in your family's peach orchard. At midnight you were awakened by "weird" noises and bright lights. You both ran to investigate. What did you find? What did you and your friend do? What did "they" do? Write a story about your adventure.

_____

_____

_____

_____

_____

_____

_____

_____

_____

_____

_____

_____

_____

_____

_____

_____

_____

_____

_____

A Rocket to _____

Activity No. 11

Student Work Sheet

Your science teacher assigned group projects. You and your two best friends decided to build a rocket—not just a model, but a real working rocket! Answer the following questions and then write a story based on your answers.

How did you build the rocket?

_____

_____

_____

What did it look like when you finished it? Draw and label it on the reverse of this page.

_____

_____

Under what circumstances did it "lift off"?

_____

_____

Where did you go? What did you see? What did you do?

_____

_____

_____

_____

What happened after you returned? What grade did your teacher give you? Why?

_____

_____

_____

Educational Impressions, Inc.

I Was Kidnapped by Aliens

Activity No. 12

Student Work Sheet

You were kidnapped by a couple of aliens. You spent forty-eight hours in captivity before managing to escape. You are now something of a local hero/heroine, with various members of the news media clamoring to interview you. Your parents have consented for you to be interviewed by one person, _____, for his/her TV show, _____.
He/she asks the following questions. How do you answer them?

What did the aliens look like? What were their names?

_____

_____

Draw and label the aliens for the audience.

I Was Kidnapped by Aliens

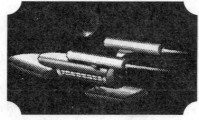

Activity No. 12, cont.   **Student Work Sheet**

Now, start at the beginning. Where were you and what were you doing when you first encountered the aliens? When was this? What was your first reaction? Your second?

_____

_____

_____

_____

_____

_____

How did the aliens take you? How did you communicate with them? How did they communicate with each other?

_____

_____

_____

_____

_____

_____

Where did the aliens take you? How did they get you there? What was the place like?

_____

_____

_____

_____

_____

_____

_____

I Was Kidnapped by Aliens

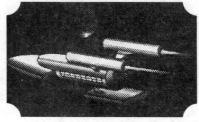

Activity No. 12, cont.   **Student Work Sheet**

What did the aliens do to you or with you while they held you captive?

_____

_____

_____

_____

_____

Did they offer you food? If so, what? How was it prepared? Did you eat it? What did it taste like?

_____

_____

_____

_____

How did you escape?

_____

_____

_____

_____

What are your feelings now about your adventure?

_____

_____

_____

Types of Science Fiction

Activity No. 13   **Student Work Sheet**

Your imagination—your ability to fantasize about alternate possibilities, your creative potential—is one of the greatest resources you have as a human being. Never fail to use your imagination because you fear that you will lose touch with reality or that others will misunderstand you or laugh at you. You can learn to enjoy and to control the powers of your imagination, and from that enjoyment and control you can learn to create science-fiction stories. The following three activities are suggestions to help you harness that powerful imagination of yours.

According to sf writers and other sf experts, there are several categories of science fiction which overlap and shade into each other. Sometimes there are no clear-cut, distinct lines. Listed below are some of those categories. If you are unfamiliar with any of the terms, check in your library for additional information. Choose a category, research that category, and write a science-fiction story of that type. Use Activities 3, 4, and 5 as a guide.

Space Opera

Hard SF

Hardcore SF

Heroic Fantasy

Pulp SF

Science Fantasy

Soft SF

Sword and Sorcery

Utopias

                                                 Educational Impressions, Inc.

Themes in Science Fiction

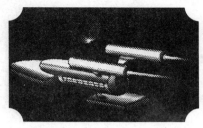

Activity No. 14   **Student Work Sheet**

The theme of a work of fiction is the main idea, the basis around which a story revolves. A story might have more than one theme. Very often science fiction will deal with universal themes, themes which have appeal to all cultures. Below is a partial list of recurring themes in science fiction. Pick one or more themes and write a science-fiction story based on the theme(s) you have chosen. Use Activities 3, 4, and 5 as a guide.

Overpopulation

Overurbanization

New Man/Mutation

Messiah or Savior

Space Travel and Exploration

Scientific and Technological Gimmickry

Time Travel (Forward or Backward)

Exploration of Human Potential

Ultimate Meaning

Adam and Eve

Alternate Worlds

Lost Worlds

Parallel Worlds

Crime and Punishment

Discovery

Invention

End of the World

Evolution

Fourth Dimension

Genetic Engineering

Colonization of Space

Devolution

Suggestions for Further Study

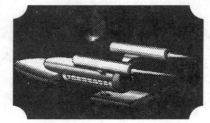

Activity No. 15

Student Work Sheet

Females in SF:

Possibly because most early sf was written for males and because most early sf writers were men, females did not fare too well in sf. Most of the roles assigned to females were stereo-types, much more so than in mainstream fiction. Influenced by the feminist movement, the roles of females in sf started to change gradually after the 1960s. Research and analyze the roles of females in early sf and later sf. Are there any differences? Are there any similarities?

Women SF Writers:

In the early days of sf, many women writers used pseudonyms or initials because publishers feared that a largely male audience would not read sf written by women. While today there are approximately nine male sf writers for every female sf writer, women are doing excellent work in the field. The female audience for sf continues to grow. Following is a very brief list of women sf writers. Choose one of them or another female sf writer to explore in depth.

Ursula K. Le Guin
J. Hunter Holly (now Joan)
Andrew North (now André)
Hilary Bailey
Jane Gaskell
Shirley Jackson
Katherine Kurtz
Doris Lessing

SF Magazines:

There are many science-fiction magazines; *Extrapolation, Foundations, Science-Fiction Studies, Galaxy, Forum, Isaac Asimov's Science Fiction,* and *Analog* are some examples. Make a compartive study of science-fiction magazines.

SF Movies:

George Melies made the first science-fiction movie, *A Trip to the Moon,* around 1900. Many sf movies have been made since then. Make a study of science-fiction movies. You might like to study sf on television also.

Suggestions for Further Study

 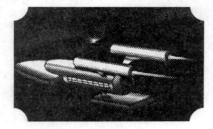
SF as Predictor:

Early science-fiction writers predicted later technological developments, such as television, space travel, atomic submarines, and labor-saving devices. Later writers had some influence on the actual development of space flight. Make a study of the science fiction of such writers as Jules Verne, H.G. Wells, Aldous Huxley, Arthur C. Clarke, Willy Lee, Issac Asimov, Frank Herbert, and Robert Heinlein. Compare their "predictions" with what has already happened and is happening today.

Juvenile SF:

Among the best known, although not the best written, juvenile science fiction was published by the Stratemeyer Syndicate. The first series, featuring the hero Tom Swift, was published between 1910 and 1938 under the name Victor Appleton. The second series, featuring Tom Swift, Jr., was published between 1954 and 1971, with the author given as Victor Appleton, Jr. Actually, several authors wrote the books, but H.G. Garis is generally credited with at least thirty-five titles in the first series. Research the history of juvenile science fiction. Then write a report comparing juvenile and adult science fiction.

Future-Problem-Solving Scenarios:

A part of the Future-Problem-Solving Program is a scenario competition. Many states have state competitions, and there is also a national competition. Winning scenarios, which are basically science-fiction stories, are published in Award-Winning Scenarios.

For information on Future Problem Solving and/or scenario writing, write to:

Dr. Anne B. Crabbe
Future Problem Solving
Coe College
Cedar Rapids, Iowa 52402

Suggestions for Further Study

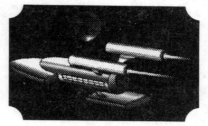

Holocaust Theme:

An often-used theme in science fiction is the world cleared by a holocaust. Only a few people remain to start the living process again. Make a study of the holocaust theme in science fiction. (Although it is not sf, *The Last Flower,* by James Thurber, should also be read.) Follow up by writing your own story.

Robinson Crusoe Theme:

The Robinson Crusoe theme has been used in sf many times. Read Daniel Defoe's *Robinson Crusoe* and then write a science-fiction story using a similar theme. Make yourself the main character.

Nowhere to Go:

The year is 3016. It is now known for certain that no life forms exist anywhere other than Earth. Many experiments to spread life into space from Earth have failed, not because the technology does not exist, but because people cannot or will not adapt psychologically. Write a story showing how Earthlings cope with the situation.

Cryonics, or I Was a Frozen Teenager:

When you were sixteen in 1999, you developed an incurable disease. As your condition worsened, you and your parents decided that cryonics presented a viable alternative to death. So you were frozen. Two hundred years later a cure is discovered for your disease. You are still seventeen when you are unfrozen. Write a story about what your life has been like since you were unfrozen.

Educational Impressions, Inc.